Plants All Around

In the space below, draw a plant you see near to your home or school. Write the names of any of the plant parts you know.

1   If you know the name of this plant, write it down here.

2   Where did you see this plant growing?

3   Write what you already know about plants.

Plants are Alive

Look at the diagrams in the table below.

1. Decide whether the diagram shows a plant (or part of a plant) or something that is not a plant. Or you may not be sure. Place a tick in the box.

	Plant or part of plant	Not a plant	Not sure
(flower)			
(car)			
(tree)			
(apple)			

Describing Plants

Collect some plants from your garden or from the market. Look at the plants and feel them.

1. Write some words to describe your plants. Place one word in each box.

Green		

2. In the space below draw and name a part of a plant that you eat.

Parts of Plants

Turn a plant out of its pot onto some newspaper. Observe it closely. Use a magnifying glass if you have one.

1   Draw your plant in the space below. Make sure you include each part of your plant.

2   Label the parts of the plant using the words from the list.

flower   leaves   roots   stem

3   Do all plants have flowers? Explain your answer.

Science Skills

Leaves - Observe it!

Look closely at two different leaves. You could use a magnifying glass if you have one.

1 How are the leaves different?

_____
_____

2 Draw one of your leaves below. Include lots of details from your observations.

3 What type of plant do your leaves come from?

_____

Observing Plants

There are many different types of plants. Some are tall, and some are small. Some plants have flowers, some plants have spiky leaves and some plants grow fruit.
Look carefully at the plants below:

1   Name one thing only the cactus has.

   _____

2   Name one thing only the geranium has.

   _____

Trees are Plants Too!

Trees may not look the same as smaller plants, but they have the same parts as other plants.

1   Find a small flowering plant and a large tree where you live.

2   Draw them below and find out what their names are.

3   Label your drawings.

4   Do the two plants have the same parts? Use the words in the list below to help you write your answer.

flower   leaves   roots   stem   trunk

Deciduous Trees

Deciduous trees lose their leaves for part of the year. In cold climates this happens in winter. In hot climates this happens in the dry season.
When all the leaves have fallen off you can see the branches and twigs.

1   Label the parts of the tree. Use the words below to help.

   branch   trunk   roots   leaves   twig   fruit

Evergreen Trees

Evergreen trees have leaves throughout the whole year.

1. Label the parts of the trees you can see in the diagrams.

Research one deciduous and one evergreen tree that grows where you live.

2. Name the trees you have chosen.

3. How do they look the same?

4. How do they look different?

More About Trees

You will need some paper, crayons, and some trees.

1 Take rubbings of the bark of some different trees in your area using crayons. Look at the different patterns you can make.

2 Now take some rubbings of the leaves and look at the different shapes.

3 Create a display of your pictures.

4 Which part of a tree is underground?

5 What happens to a deciduous tree?

6 Name an evergreen tree that grows where you live.

Plants and Their Parts

Plants can look very different, but they all have the same main parts.

1 What parts do most plants have? List them below.

_____
_____
_____

2 What other plant parts do you know? Write as many as you can below.

_____
_____
_____

Plants we Eat

Class 1 made a pictogram showing the different fruits the class had eaten that day.

1   How many oranges did the class eat that day?

2   Which fruit did the class like the most?

3   Name three more fruits.

Science Skills

Fruit – Record it!

Carry out a survey to find out which fruits your class like the best.

1. Make a tally first.

Fruit	Tally	Total

2. Then make a pictogram below of your results.

6				
5				
4				
3				
2				
1				
	apple	banana	grape	orange

Plant Identification Kit

Make an identification kit to help others identify a plant in your area.

1. In the space below, draw a picture of your favourite plant.

The name of this plant is _____.

2. Label the plant parts.
3. Write some sentences that describe your plant to help others find and identify it.

_____
_____
_____

Making a Model of a Plant

1. Explain how to make a model plant. First make a list of the materials you will need. Then write some instructions.

For the flower you will need:

For the stem or trunk and branches you will need:

For the leaves you will need:

For the roots you will need:

Instructions

What Have I Learned?

Go back to the first picture you drew at the beginning of this book.

Use a different colour to add to your first picture all the new things you have learned.

Add one of these faces next to each statement to show how you feel about the sentences below.

Yes	Not yet	Sometimes
🙂	🙁	😐

I know the names of some common plants.	
I know what deciduous and evergreen trees are.	
I can point to the stem, trunk, roots, leaves, flowers and blossoms of plants and trees.	